RIFT
raiders

RIFT raiders

WRITTEN BY **mark sable**

ART BY **julian totino tedesco**

COLORS BY **juanmanuel tumburus**

DESIGN & LETTERS BY **bill tortolini**

EDITED BY **jimmy palmiotti**

PRODUCED BY **kickstart comic inc.**

COVER BY **julian totino tedesco & bill tortolini**

KICKSTART

For Kickstart Comics Inc.:
Samantha Shear, Managing Editor

WELL, WHATEVER, I'M SURE I CAN PAWN IT ON E-BAY FOR--

CLANG

OKAY, OKAY. THAT WAS A *GOOD* THING. I ESCAPED BEING CHOPPED IN HALF BY A MASSIVE BLADE-THINGY.

NOW ALL I HAVE TO DO IS CATCH MY BREATH.

I'M SURE I CAN PUT EVERYTHING BACK THE WAY IT WAS BEFORE MY PARENTS GET HOME.

WE DON'T LEAVE UNTIL *TOMORROW*, GENIUS.

NOW HAND IT OVER.

I DON'T KNOW WHAT YOU'RE TALKING ABOUT. AND IF I DID... REVEALING ITS LOCATION WOULD INVOLVE YOU FINALLY TAKING ME SOMEWHERE COOL.

NOT YOUR CONCERN. WHAT *IS* YOUR CONCERN IS THAT HE'S *NOT* CRACKING.

...SED ...OVER ....

...N ...HER ...E'LL ...I POP.

WHAT?!

AND DO CLEAN YOUR UNIFORM. WE HAVE *STANDARDS* HERE.

IS THIS SOME KIND OF JOKE?

I, KNOW, IT SEEMS LIKE A SILLY THING TO RISK A BEATING FROM SIKES OVER, BUT IT'S ALL I HAVE LEFT FROM MY PARENTS.

MINE WEREN'T *TREASURE HUNTERS*. JUST... HISTORIANS.

GETTING HIT BY SIKES WAS JUST AN ACT, WASN'T IT? THIS IS JUST ANOTHER TRICK TO GET MY PARENTS...I DON'T EVEN KNOW WHAT IT IS. WHAT ARE YOU PLAYING AT, DUDE?

YOU THINK I'D MAKE UP THE FACT MY PARENTS *DIED IN A TRAIN WRECK*? OR--WAIT? WHY IS YOUR SHIRT *GLOWING*?

IT LOOKS LIKE THESE THINGS FIT TOGETHER.

NO KIDDING.

BUT WHATEVER IT IS, IT'S MISSING--

THIS?

GRAB THEM.

YOU'VE HAD THAT THE WHOLE TIME, SIKES? THE WARDEN'S GOING TO *KILL* YOU WHEN HE FINDS OUT YOU'VE BEEN HOLDING OUT ON US.

TRUST ME, HE WON'T.

KRRZZZZZ

NOW, IF YOU'LL ALL EXCUSE ME, I'VE GOT SOME*WHEN* ELSE TO BE—

WHAT WAS THAT?

SWOOPING CRANE KICK. SHAOLIN MONKS TAUGHT ME THAT BACK IN 1560.

THIS IS ME DANCING LIKE A BUTTERFLY—

—AND STINGING LIKE A BEE. MOHAMMED ALI, 1975.

THUCK!

LET ME ~ESS—BILLY THE KID, 1881.

WILD BILL HICKOCK. 1876. RIGHT BEFORE *THE DEAD MAN'S HAND.* BUT NICE GUESS, MYLES.

SIKES, HAND OVER YOUR PARTS OF THE *CHRONOS* DEVICE.

WHO *ARE* YOU?

THIS CENTURY? *LAYLA.* GREATEST WARRIOR OF ALL TIME.

THE WHAT?

OH, LIKE YOU DON'T KNOW. THIS IS THE SECOND TIME YOU'VE ACTIVATED IT, DODGER.

HOW DO YOU KNOW WHO WE—

WOULD YOU MIND PUTTING THE LAST PIECE IN? MY HANDS ARE KIND OF FULL AND I HAVEN'T GOT MUCH TIME TO GET YOU OUT OF HERE.

NOBUNAGA. WITH A LITTLE ASSIST FROM *SIR ROBIN OF LOCKSLEY.*

HOP

THOSE GAUNTLETS—

WILL BE AROUND YOUR NECK, IF YOU DON'T PUT THE DEVICE YOU "DIDN'T STEAL" IN THEM.

—I SAW THEM GRAB MY PARENTS IN THE CRASH. I MAY NOT KNOW WHAT THIS IS, OR WHAT'S GOING ON, BUT I DO KNOW ONE THING.

YOU'RE. *NOT.* GETTING THIS.

GZZZ

NICE! NOW LET'S GET GOING. MY HOURGLASS WAS PROGRAMMED WITH THE COORDINATES OF A...SAFE-HAVEN.

YOU'RE TAKING SIKES?

THE FENCE'S RDERS. BRING LL FOUR OF U...OR NONE AT ALL.

POOM

THE FENCE?

DUDE. I CAN'T SPLIT *BULLETS* IN HALF WITH MY SWORD. LESS QUESTIONS, MORE JUMPING THROUGH RIFTS IN TIME.

RANDED SOMEWHERE OUT THERE IN TIME. 'CKED AN INSTANT BEFORE THEIR APPAR- T DEATHS BY **THE CASIMIR**—THE MAN WHO S HOLDING YOU IN THAT ORPHANAGE."

L IN AN ATTEMPT TO GET WHAT CH OF THEM LEFT TO YOU. ? TO WHAT YOU, DODGER, ARE LDING IN YOUR HANDS."

"THE **CHRONOS DEVICE.** SOMETHING YOUR PARENTS, THE CASIMIR AND I INVENTED."

THE FUTURE.

"AS YOU'VE SEEN, IT OPENS **RIFTS** IN TIME...AND ALLOWED US —AND ONLY US—TO TRAVEL THROUGH THEM."

HEN HOW WERE **WE** BLE TO USE IT?"

"TO PREVENT MISUSE—IT WAS KEYED TO OUR **DNA.** THE FRAGMENTS OF THE DEVICE WERE ONLY **PART** OF YOUR INHERITANCE."

"THE CASIMIR WASN'T JUST STEALING THINGS, E WAS COLLECTING **DEADLY WEAPONS**, GATHERING A **POWERFUL ARMY**, AND USING HEM TO WELL...CONQUER TIME AND SPACE."

WHY?

"SOME SAY THAT IT WAS BECAUSE HE CAME FROM A **TIME** AND PLACE WHERE WAR AND CRIME WERE THINGS OF THE PAST. THAT HE WAS SIMPLY **BORED**."

"BUT I TOO CAME FROM THAT PLACE, AND FOUND A...HEALTHIER OUTLET FOR **MY** BOREDOM. I THINK THAT IT WAS SOME-THING IN THE CASIMIR'S **CHILDHOOD**."

"WHATEVER THE REASON, WHEN YOUR PARENTS DISCOVERED THE CASIMIR'S PLAN-"

"THE CASIMIR HAD TO **ELIMINATE** THEM."

"AFTER HE...DISPOSED OF LAYLA'S PARENTS, THE SURVIVORS FLED."

"ONCE YOU WERE SAFE, THEY TRIED TO STOP THE CASIMIR."

"THEY KNEW WHAT WEAPONS HE USED TO DECLARE WAR IN THE FUTURE, AND TRIED TO GATHER THEM FIRST."

JERUSALEM: JUDEA, 26 A.D.

"I NEED YOU—THEY NEED YOU—TO FIND THE OTHERS."

SO WE CAN USE THIS TO FIND OUR PARENTS?

EVENTUALLY, YES. I'LL EVEN HELP YOU, BUT YOU'VE GOT TO STOP THE CASIMIR FIRST. YOU'VE ALREADY SEEN THE ARMY HE'S BEEN TRAINING AT THE ORPHANAGE.

I NEED YOU TO GET THE MYSTICAL WEAPONS THE CASIMIR'S BEEN SEEKING BEFORE HE DOES.

WHY US?

AND WHY CAN'T WE RESCUE OUR PARENTS FIRST?

NO OFFENSE, BUT THE CHRONOS DEVICE WAS OUR INHERITANCE, NOT YOURS. IT'S REALLY NOT YOUR DECISION TO MAKE WHICH ORDER WE GRAB THINGS.

CUTE AS YOU ARE, I'M NOT AFRAID TO USE THIS. YOUR PARENTS WOULD BE THE ONES STOPPING THE CASIMIR IF NOT FOR YOU. WE DO IT THE FENCE'S WAY—OR NOT AT ALL.

EASY, LAYLA. APOLOGIES. I RAISED THE GIRL, AND WHILE I ADMIRE HER LOYALTY...THOSE ARE FAIR QUESTIONS.

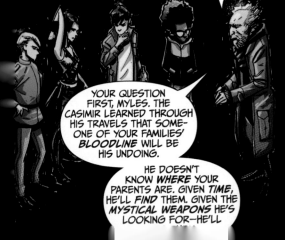

AS LONG AS THE CASIMIR BELIEVES YOUR PARENTS ARE DEAD, HE THINKS HE HAS NO ENEMIES.

THAT GIVES YOU THE ADVANTAGE OF STEALING WEAPONS BEFORE HE EVEN KNOWS YOU'RE LOOKING FOR THEM.

YOUR QUESTION FIRST, MYLES. THE CASIMIR LEARNED THROUGH HIS TRAVELS THAT SOME- ONE OF YOUR FAMILIES' BLOODLINE WILL BE HIS UNDOING.

HE DOESN'T KNOW WHERE YOUR PARENTS ARE. GIVEN TIME, HE'LL FIND THEM. GIVEN THE MYSTICAL WEAPONS HE'S LOOKING FOR—HE'LL

WON'T *STEALING* THESE ARTIFACTS--FOR GOOD OR ILL--MESS UP HISTORY?

PERHAPS *THIS* WILL REASSURE YOU.

THIS IS A FOUR DIMENSIONAL *TIME MAP*. IF YOU KNOW HOW TO READ IT, YOU CAN SEE THE OUTCOME OF EVERY POSSIBLE EVENT.

EACH OF YOUR MISSIONS--SHOULD YOU CHOOSE TO ACCEPT THEM--WILL BE CAREFULLY PLOTTED (BY ME, OF COURSE).

IF YOU DO EXACTLY AS I SAY, NOT ONLY WON'T YOU SCREW WITH HISTORY... YOU'LL ACTUALLY *IMPROVE* IT.

WHAT ARE YOUR RULES, EXACTLY?

WOW, YOU REALLY ARE LIKE YOUR PARENTS. THEY BELIEVED IN CHANGING ABSOLUTELY NOTHING. I'M A BIT MORE...LIBERAL.

DON'T TAKE ANYTHING YOU CAN'T REPLACE WITH A REASONABLE FACSIMILE THEREOF. GUARD YOUR IDENTITIES CAREFULLY. *LAYLA'S* BEEN DOING THIS FOR A WHILE NOW, SHE'LL FILL YOU IN ON THE REST AS YOU GO.

WHAT'S IN IT FOR YOU?

ASIDE FROM THE FACT THE CASIMIR WANTS ME *DEAD?* AND THAT EVEN THOUGH I'M SAFE FROM HIM HERE, I CAN NEVER *LEAVE* THIS GODFORSAKEN PLACE?

MAYBE IF I HELP YOU STOP THE CASIMIR, YOUR PARENTS WILL LET ME GO FREE. THINK OF THIS AS MY PENANCE.

OF COURSE, IF *MY* OFFER DOESN'T INTEREST YOU, I WON'T *FORCE* YOU. I'M HAPPY TO SEND YOU BACK TO THAT SCHOOL--

ROME, 1503. THE PALACE OF *CESARE BORGIA.*

"I THOUGHT YOU'D SEE THINGS MY WAY."

I DON'T GET IT... NONE OF THE WEAPONS ON THE FENCE'S LIST *EVER* EXISTED.

NEITHER DID TIME TRAVEL UNTIL YESTERDAY.

EASY. IN AND OUT. BORGIA'S MEN OUTNUMBER US TEN-TO-ONE, AND WE'RE NOT LOOKING FOR A FIGHT.

SPEAK FOR YOURSELF.

JUST TRUST ME.

THESE CREATURES— THEY CAN'T EXIST! THERE WOULD BE A FOSSIL RECORD.

NOT IF WE GRAB THEM FIRST.

ACCORDING TO THE FENCE, MAN WHO BECAME KNOWN AS PERSEUS, WAS THE GREATEST *GENETIC ENGINEER* OF THE CLASSICAL ERA--

--UNTIL HE SUFFERED A MYSTERIOUS CONCUSSION, HIS KNOWLEDGE WAS LOST TO THE CENTURIES, AND HIS CREATIONS DISAPPEARED INTO "MYTH".

OTHERWISE KNOWN AS *THE FENCE'S VAULT.*

SORRY SIKES.

I MAY HAVE TO *WORK* WITH YOU.

BUT THAT DOESN'T MEAN I HAVE TO TRUST YOU WITH *THIS.*

¿?

I WOULD HAVE PREFERRED IT *INTACT*, BUT AT LEAST THE SOUTH WON'T BE WINNING THE CIVIL WAR WITH GATLING'S *STEAMPUNK EXO-SKELETONS.*

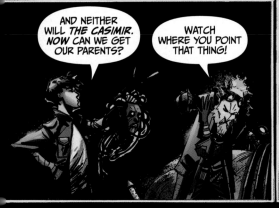

AND NEITHER WILL *THE CASIMIR. NOW* CAN WE GET OUR PARENTS?

WATCH WHERE YOU POINT THAT THING!

AND DON'T GET *TOO COCKY*, THESE MISSIONS WERE JUST WARM UPS.

THE LAST ITEM ON MY LIST IS THE MOST POWERFUL WEAPON OF THEM ALL.

GR!ZZZ

YOU... YOU D-D-DON'T HAVE TO D-D-DO THIS.

ISN'T *TRAVELING* THROUGH TIME REWARD ENOUGH?

SAYS THE MAN WHO'S SPENT HIS LIFE *PLUNDERING* IT.

THESE CHILDREN... THEY CAN BE USED FOR SO MUCH *MORE*. THEY CAN BE USED TO *CHANGE* THE PAST. TO CHANGE *YOUR* PAST. TO *REDEEM* YOU.

IT WAS *YOUR* IDEA TO USE THEM. I WOULD PREFER THEM [DE]AD LIKE THEIR PARENTS. [BU]T WITH THEM OUT OF MY [W]AY, AND THE CHILDREN [GA]THERING MY WEAPONS... THE FUTURE IS MINE.

DON'T MAKE ME RECONSIDER SPARING THEM. IT'S *HUMILIATING* SEEING THOSE BRATS [A]GAIN. I WILL *NOT* ALLOW THEM TO BRING ABOUT MY DOOM.

DON'T WORRY, OUR *DEAL* IS STILL ON. YOU'LL GET YOUR FREEDOM—

ZZZ

—WHEN I GET—

AND IN ALL THAT TIME, YOU NEVER ASKED HIM HOW HE GOT HIS *NAME*?

SURE, HE'S BEEN SELLING STUFF ON THE SIDE. JUST LIKE SIKES AND DODGER HAVE BEEN POCKETING A LITTLE ON EACH OF OUR TRIPS.

THE MONA LISAS...AND COME ON, DON'T TELL ME YOU ALL HAVEN'T THOUGHT ABOUT COMING BACK FOR *THE GRAIL*.

BUT THE CASIMIR *THE REASON* TH FENCE CAN'T LEAV THE TESSERAC. WHY WOULD HE HELP HIM?

THAT'S JUST IT. HE'S *USING US* TO BUY HIS FREEDOM.

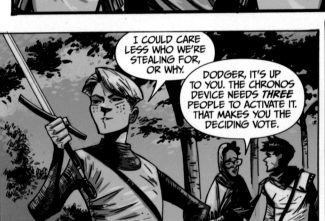

I COULD CARE LESS WHO WE'RE STEALING FOR, OR WHY.

DODGER, IT'S UP TO YOU. THE CHRONOS DEVICE NEEDS *THREE* PEOPLE TO ACTIVATE IT. THAT MAKES YOU THE DECIDING VOTE.

EVEN IF WHAT YOU'RE S IS TRUE, IF THE CHOIC BETWEEN STEALING MYSTICAL ARTIFACTS BEING STUCK IN THA SCHOOL—

I LIKED IT THERE JUST FINE.

I BELIEVE YOU MYLES, BUT IF WE GO BACK TO THE FENCE, WE CAN ALWAYS CONFRONT HIM.

AND IT WON'T HURT TO HAVE EXCALIBUR WHEN WE DO SO. CAN WE ALL AT LEAST AGREE ON THAT?

IF ANY OF YOU LAY A FINGER, LET ALONE A *SWORD*, ON THE FENCE—ESPECIALLY YOU *SIKES*, I'LL—

I'M JUST VOTING TO RETURN TO A TIME WITH *INDOOR PLUMBING*. IF I HAVE TO WIPE ONE MORE TIME WITH—WHAT ARE YOU ALL STARING AT?

SEE! THE FENCE WASN'T LYING. THERE'S NO WAY HE WOULD BE IN LEAGUE WITH THE CASIMIR.

EXCUSE ME. DID YOU SAY THAT YOU *KNEW MY PARENTS*?

LUCKILY WE STILL HAVE THE FRAGMENT *YOU* LEFT US WITH. IT WON'T ALLOW US TO GO WHEREVER WE LIKE, BUT WE SHOULD BE ABLE TO FOLLOW YOUR FRIEND.

YES. THEY HELPED US INVENT—

I'M AFRAID MYLES IS RIGHT, LAYLA. *THE FENCE*—WITH OUR SON'S UNWITTING AID—IS THE ONE WHO PLUCKED US FROM THE TIME STREAM AND EXILED US HERE.

JUST AS HE DID *YOUR* PARENTS.

THEY'RE STILL ALIVE?

SOMEWHERE, SOME*WHEN*—YES.

ONCE WE FIND SIKES AND HAVE A FULLY FUNCTIONAL *CHRONOS DEVICE*, WE'LL GO STRAIGHT AFTER THE FENCE AND GET YOUR PARENTS LOCATION SO WE CAN—

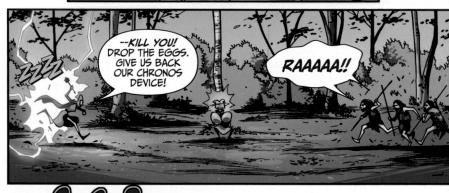

YOU *LIED* TO US. TO *ME!*

KRJ-7OK

WE'VE GOT SOME *QUESTIONS.*

WHAT DO YOU WANT ME TO SAY? YES, *I* KIDNAPPED YOUR PARENTS.

I'D BE VERY CAREFUL WITH YOUR ANSWERS. YOU KNOW BETTER THAN ANYONE HOW STRONG LAYLA IS. NOT SURE HOW LONG I CAN HOLD HER BACK.

CLANG

THOSE WEREN'T THE *CASIMIR'S* HANDS IN THE GAUNTLETS THAT GRABBED MY PARENTS FROM THE RIFT. THEY WERE *YOURS!* HAVE AT HIM, LAYLA.

I DID IT TO KEEP THEM *SAFE* FROM THE CASIMIR.

THEN WHY WERE YOU *SELLING* HIM ARTIFACTS? *WEAPONS.* THE ONES *WE STOLE.*

TO *STALL* HIM.

WHILE I PREPARED YOU FOR THE *FINAL BATTLE.* THE ONE WHERE YOU ARE DESTINED TO--

IT'S ONE THING FOR MY *PARENTS* TO LAY A GUILT TRIP ON ME. I DON'T HAVE TO TAKE THIS FROM YOU.

NONE OF US DO. HOLD HIS GAUNTLETS BEHIND HIS BACK. THIS TIME I'M TAKING HIS HEAD CLEAN OFF.

ALL THESE YEARS LAYLA, I'VE BEEN LIKE A *FATHER* TO YOU.

ONLY BECAUSE YOU GOT RID OF MY *REAL* PARENTS.

I *DIDN'T* GET RID OF THEM. THEY PLACED YOU IN MY CARE, AND THEY *ASKED ME* TO HIDE THEM.

YOU CAN'T KILL HIM, LAYLA.

WHY, BECAUSE THAT "ISN'T ME"? YOU HAVEN'T KNOWN ME LONG ENOUGH TO --

MY PARENTS DID SAY YOURS WERE STILL ALIVE. IF THE FENCE CAN GIVE US THEIR LOCATION—

THAT'S THE ONE THING I *CAN'T* DO.

WHY NOT? WHO THE *HELL* DO YOU THINK YOU ARE?

IF YOU TRY TO RESCUE THEM ON YOUR OWN—

—YOU'LL ONLY *LEAD* THE CASIMIR TO THEM.

KILL ME IF YOU WANT, BUT I WON'T HELP YOU GO TO YOUR DEATHS.

DODGER, CAN YOU REALLY BREAK INTO *ANYTHING*?

MY PARENTS SPENT THEIR LIFE KEEPING THINGS FROM ME. I SPENT MINE UNCOVERING THEM.

THERE'S A FOUR DIMENSIONAL MAP IN THERE THAT HE USED TO PLAN OUR MISSIONS. IF YOU CAN GET TO IT—

I CAN READ IT... AND PINPOINT OUR PARENTS' LOCATIONS.

YOU'RE MAKING A HUGE MISTAKE.

SAVE YOUR BREATH—

—OR YOU'LL RUN OUT OF AIR BEFORE WE GET BACK.

WHOSE PARENTS DO WE GO AFTER FIRST?

LET'S RESCUE MINE *LAST*. THEY'LL ONLY TRY TO *STOP* US AGAIN.

I...I'M NOT SURE I'M READY. MY PARENTS *ABANDONED* ME—

WELL THEN. GET READY TO MEET *MINE*. HOPE YOU BROUGHT YOUR SUN BLOCK.

KRIZ

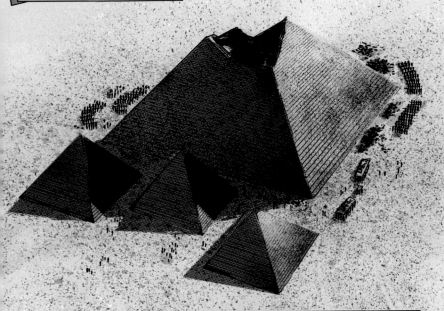

THE GIZA NECROPOLIS, EGYPT.
TWENTY-THREE HUNDRED YEARS
BEFORE THE COMMON ERA.

MOM!
DAD!

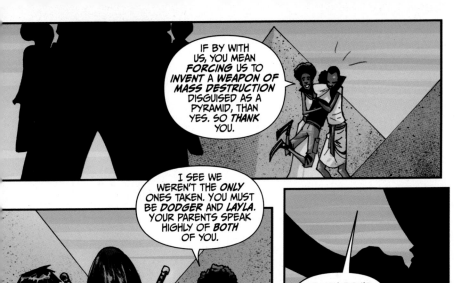

IF BY WITH US, YOU MEAN *FORCING* US TO INVENT A WEAPON OF *MASS DESTRUCTION* DISGUISED AS A PYRAMID, THAN YES. SO *THANK* YOU.

I SEE WE WEREN'T THE *ONLY* ONES TAKEN. YOU MUST BE *DODGER* AND *LAYLA*. YOUR PARENTS SPEAK HIGHLY OF *BOTH* OF YOU.

IF YOU DON'T BELIEVE ME, YOU CAN ASK THEM YOURSELF.

I IMAGINE IF YOU GOT HERE, YOU MUST HAVE A FUNCTIONING CHRONOS DEVICE.

WHAT ABOUT THE PYRAMID YOU'VE BEEN BUILDING? WE CAN'T JUST LEAVE IT HERE.

WE BUILT IT TO *SELF-DESTRUCT*. YOU SAVED US FROM BEING CAUGHT IN THE BLAST. SHALL WE?

KAFWIZZ

PROHIBITION ERA CHICAGO.

WE THOUGHT WE'D BE ABLE TO COME BACK FOR YOU SOONER. BUT WE'VE BEEN *TRAPPED* HERE FOR *SIXTEEN YEARS*.

WHY ARE *WE* SUCH A THREAT TO THE CASIMIR?

BECAUSE HE'S BEEN TO THE FUTURE. HE'S *FROM THERE*. AND HE'S SEEN YOU DEFEAT HIM.

SO THE FENCE IS ON *OUR* SIDE?

VERY MUCH SO. WHY, DID SOMETHING *HAPPEN* TO HIM?

WELL—

NEVER MIND HIM. WE'VE STILL GOT TO RESCUE *MY* PARENTS. AND HAVE YOU EXPLAIN TO THEM HOW I'M NOT A SCREW UP, THAT ALL THIS ISN'T MY FAULT AND THAT I'M DESTINED TO SAVE THE—

WE GET IT!

WHAT ARE YOU DOING?

SIMPLE. WE JUST GO BACK RIGHT BEFORE THE CASIMIR GRABBED THEM AND—

IT'S ANYTHING *BUT* SIMPLE. THE CASIMIR *WANTED* ARTHUR TO SEE YOUR PARENTS ABDUCTED.

MY DAUGHTER TAKES AFTER US, SO WE'RE ANYTHING BUT COWARDS.

BUT THERE'S A DIFFERENCE BETWEEN COWARDICE AND STUPIDITY. THE MINUTE WE GO BACK FOR YOUR PARENTS, HE'LL GRAB *US* INSTEAD OF THEM.

IT DOESN'T HAVE TO BE "US". I'LL GO BACK. ALL I NEED IS TWO OF YOUR HANDS TO ACTIVATE IT. I'LL GO BACK ALONE, AND YOU CAN SEND ME BACK.

I HAVE *EXCALIBUR*. I'LL FACE THE CASIMIR MYSELF.

NO.

AFTER ALL I'VE DONE FOR YOU GUYS?

JUST ASK YOURSELF THIS QUESTION. WOULD YOU LET ANY OF *US* GO BACK ALONE?

AS MUCH AS IT KILLS ME TO SAY THIS, WE NEED THE FENCE.

WE DO IT THE SMART WAY. THE TESSERACT IS THE ONE PLACE THE CASIMIR CAN'T GET TO.

KA KRIZ

WAIT, WHAT DO *YOU* MEAN YOU HAVE EXCALIBUR? WHAT AM *I* HOLDING? NO *WONDER* CAMELOT FELL...

FWIZZZISHHH

LOOKING FOR ME?

WHAT DID YOU DO WITH THE FENCE, SIKES?

ASKS THE GUY WHO *TIED HIM UP* AND *LOCKED HIM* IN AN *AIRTIGHT VAULT.*

DON'T WORRY, YOU'LL JOIN HIM SOON ENOUGH.

CRIZZZ

SHUNK

WE KNEW YOU'D DO IT!

YOU *DID?* YOU MEAN YOU PEEKED IN THE FUTURE LIKE I DID?

WELL, WE *ARE* TIME TRAVELERS.

WE SHOULDN'T HAVE KEPT THIS FROM YOU. WE SHOULD HAVE BELIEVED.

I ASSUME THIS MEANS I DON'T HAVE TO GO BACK TO THAT SCHOOL.

NO ONE DOES, OR EVER *WILL*. IN FACT, CLOSING THAT PLACE DOWN SHOULD BE OUR FIRST TRIP BACK IN TIME. AS A FAMILY.

WHAT ABOUT THEM?

THE FENCE HAS PROVED WHOSE SIDE HE'S ON. HE'S THE PERSON WE OWE THE SECOND BIGGEST APOLOGY.

AS FOR *SIKES*... I THINK *PERMANENT EXILE* IN THE TESSERACT SHOULD PROVE SUFFICIENT.

BONUS
sketchbook

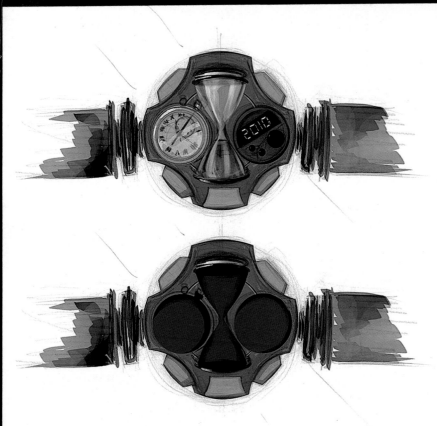

by Julian Totino Tedesco

Layla

Dodger

Sikes

The
Warden

The
Fence

RIFT raiders

KICKSTART

LOS ANGELES • CALIFORNIA